MOBILITY TRAINING

by Norman Brook

About the Author

Norman Brook was appointed B.A.A.B. National Coach for Northern Ireland in 1982. He was born and educated in Scotland where he also taught as a Secondary School Teacher. In 1978 he returned to higher education to study Coaching Science at Dunfermline College of Physical Education (Edinburgh) and at Lakehead University (Canada).

Norman has coached athletes to Great Britain International honours and has been a coach to Great Britain and Northern Ireland Teams since 1982.

This booklet follows on from the original edition by Peter Harper which was published with the title 'Mobility Exercises' in 1971.

Norman Brook

Ernie Williams

About the Illustrator

Ernie Williams is Senior Teacher of Art at Mundella College, Leicester. A keen athlete who regularly competes in the veterans sections of running events, he is also actively involved in orienteering. He was previously commissioned to provide the artwork for the AAA Five Star Award Scheme.

'Mobility Exercises' (Peter Harper) 1971

'Mobility Training' (Norman Brook) First Edition 1986 This Edition 1990

Designed, typeset in Times Roman and printed on 115gsm Fineblade Cartridge by Reedprint Ltd, Windsor, Berkshire, England.

Contents

ISBN 0 85134 079 2

3M/17M/06/90

CHAPTER 1

INTRODUCTION TO MOBILITY AND ITS ROLE

Athletics allows the individual the opportunity of expressing himself physically through movements such as running, hurdling, jumping, vaulting and throwing. As coaches we assess each athlete primarily through his competitive success and/or the times, distances or heights he achieves. To effect improvement, we direct our attention to the underlying qualities that determine competitive performance. One such quality is the athlete's level of skill, his ease, accuracy and range of movement. Any pattern of movement, be it running, hurdling, jumping, vaulting or throwing, involves a series of coordinated joint actions. Running, for example, involves the extension and flexion of ankle, knee, hip and elbow joints, and rotation of the shoulder joint. The extent to which an athlete can achieve a full range of movement is determined by his level of mobility. *Mobility is the capacity to perform joint actions through a wide range of movement.* Poor mobility implies restricted range of movement, with poor skill levels, inefficient patterns of movement and performances below an athlete's potential. A good level of mobility permits free movement allowing the athlete to express himself fully. Good mobility is essential for success in athletics.

This booklet presents a comprehensive catalogue of mobility exercises. The first three chapters explain the types and role of mobility, the scientific basis of mobility, and the principles of mobility training. Chapter Four lists mobility exercises, classified according to the joint actions involved. Specific mobility exercises for each athletic discipline are illustrated in Chapter Five.

Types of Mobility

In the introduction, mobility was defined as the capacity to perform joint actions through a wide range of movement. To help illustrate the different types of mobility, we will consider one particular joint action, hip flexion.

This action and that of the opposite action, hip extension, are shown in diagram 1. The diagram also illustrates two groups of muscles, those to the front which flex the hip and those to the rear which extend the hip. When one group contracts, the opposite group has to relax to make the movement of flexion or extension possible. Those muscles which contract to cause the movement are called the protagonists, whilst those muscles which relax to make the movement possible are called the antagonists. In mobility training, when you perform an exercise it is the antagonist muscles that are stretched.

An athlete can perform a mobility exercise (1) by actively contracting his protagonist muscles to perform the exercise, or (2) he can be completely passive and let some external assistance such as a training partner move the limbs into a position which places the antagonist muscles on stretch. Mobility exercises can therefore be either active (movement caused by the active contraction of the protagonist muscle) or passive (movement caused by an external force – protagonist muscle relaxed).

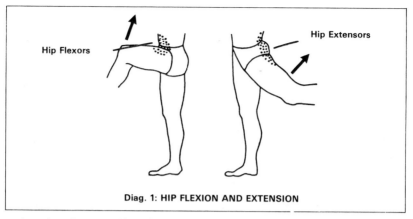

Diag. 1: HIP FLEXION AND EXTENSION

Hip Flexors

Hip Extensors

Another factor which determines the type of mobility is the speed at which the exercise is being performed. Exercises can be performed slowly with a sustained stretching of the antagonist muscles, or they can be performed quickly with a bouncy, ballistic action. Active exercises can be performed either as slow static movements or as fast dynamic movements. Passive exercises must always be performed slowly and never dynamically. (Great care has to be taken with passive exercises as the athlete does not always have complete control of the exercise). In order to differentiate between active slow stretch and active fast stretch exercises, the term active is used for slow stretch exercises only and the term kinetic is used for fast stretch exercises. There are, therefore, three types of mobility: active, passive and kinetic.

The Role of Mobility

If athletes are to learn and utilise effectively the techniques associated with their events and are to avoid injury successfully, they require a good level of mobility. An athlete will find it difficult, if not impossible, to learn a new technique if his mobility is poor. The coach might mistakenly put the lack of progress down to a lack of strength or poor coordination, when in fact the athlete is not capable of assuming a required position due to a lack of mobility. A good level of mobility is also essential for the development of specific conditioning (i.e. the application of strength or speed in a particular event). Poor mobility will also make training for other types of conditioning difficult and will reduce an athlete's potential for improvement.

In some events such as shot, discus and javelin, the athlete needs to apply force to the implement over the longest possible range. A lack of mobility will reduce the effective range over which force can be applied. The range of movement over which a force can be applied is often used as a definition for mobility. This is actually a good definition for athletics, as there is little point in an athlete having a good range of movement if he is weak throughout the range.

Even in endurance events, where the actual ranges of movement may be limited, good mobility is essential as it allows free, efficient movement. The athlete will be able to develop a good, effective technique which in turn will reduce energy demands placed on the athlete.

3

Athletes who lack mobility have an increased risk of injury. Muscles, tendons, ligaments and other connective tissue can be damaged when an athlete attempts to exceed his normal range of movement. Strains can also develop as a result of cumulative stress placed on muscles or connective tissue, due to compensatory muscular work taking place to accommodate an athlete's lack of mobility.

All athletes require a basic level of general or all-round mobility to allow them to accept and benefit from other forms of training. In addition to this, individual athletes will need to develop mobility further for those joint actions involved in the techniques of their events.

CHAPTER 2

SCIENTIFIC BASIS OF MOBILITY

A basic understanding of the anatomy, biomechanics and physiology of mobility is essential for the coach who wishes to plan an effective mobility programme. In this chapter the various joints and their actions are explained, as are those other factors which influence an athlete's range of joint movement.

Types of Joints

The human skeleton is made up of a number of different bones forming the scaffolding on which the body is supported (diagram 2). The points at which two or more bones meet are the joints. Some joints are completely immoveable, others are slightly moveable and the rest, the ones about which we are mainly concerned, are freely moveable (diagram 3). Synovial joint is another term used for a freely moveable joint.

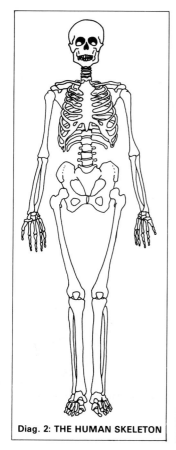

Diag. 2: THE HUMAN SKELETON

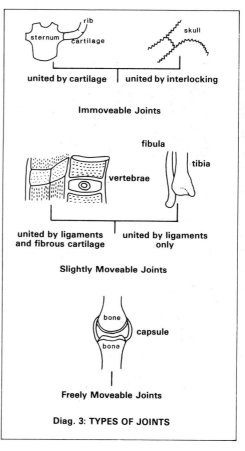

Diag. 3: TYPES OF JOINTS

5

There are six types of freely moveable or synovial joint:

i   *Plane or Gliding Joint*

Permits sliding movements such as those occuring in the small bones of the wrist or in spinal movements. Flat surfaces are in contact.

Diag. 4: PLANE OR GLIDING JOINT

ii   *Saddle Joint*

Permits flexion, extension, abduction, adduction and to a limited extent circumduction. The carpometacarpal joint of the thumb is the only saddle joint in the body. Concave-convex surfaces are in contact.

Diag. 5: SADDLE JOINT

iii   *Hinge Joint*

Permits flexion and extension only. The knee and elbow joints are examples.

iv   *Pivot Joint*

Diag. 6: HINGE JOINT

Permits rotation in a transverse plane about a longitudinal axis. An example is the joint between the upper ends of the radius and the ulna.

Diag. 7: PIVOT JOINT

v   *Condyloid Joint*

Permits a small amount of extension, flexion, abduction, adduction and circumduction. An example would be the wrist joint.

vi   *Ball and Socket Joint*

Diag. 8: CONDYLOID JOINT

Permits a wide range of movement in flexion, extension, abduction, adduction, and circumduction. A spherical head fits into a cup-like cavity. Examples are hip and shoulder joints.

Diag. 9: BALL AND SOCKET JOINT

Planes and Axes

Joint actions are described in relation to the so called anatomical position illustrated in diagram 10. Movement is defined by referring to the three planes and the three axes shown in the diagram.

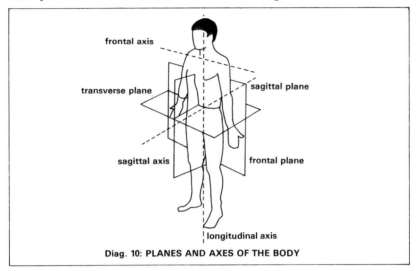

Diag. 10: PLANES AND AXES OF THE BODY

The Three Planes

i   *Sagittal Plane*

A vertical plane which passes from front to rear dividing the body into two symmetrical halves.

ii   *Frontal Plane*

A vertical plane which passes from side to side at right angles to the sagittal plane.

iii   *Transverse Plane*

Any horizontal plane which lies parallel to the diaphragm.

The Three Axes

i   *Frontal Axis* (Rotation in the frontal plane)

Passes horizontally from side to side at right angles to the sagittal plane.

ii   *Sagittal Axis* (Rotation in the sagittal plane)

Passes from front to rear lying at right angles to the frontal plane.

iii   *Longitudinal Axis* (Vertical Axis) (Rotation in the transverse plane)

Passes from head to feet at right angles to the transverse plane.

Joint Actions

A number of different actions are possible in the various freely moveable joints. The structure of the joint determines how it functions and which different actions are possible. The planes and axes of the anatomical position are used to describe each of the joint actions. A number of joint actions are described and illustrated:

Movement in the Sagittal Plane about Frontal Axis

Diag. 11: FLEXION

Diag. 12: EXTENSION

Flexion

The angle of the joint decreases. At the ankle joint this action is called dorsi-flexion.

Extension

The angle of the joint increases. At the ankle joint the action is called plantar-flexion.

Movements in the Frontal Plane about a Sagittal Axis

Diag. 13: ABDUCTION

Diag. 14: ADDUCTION

Abduction

Movement away from the midline of the body.

Adduction

Movement towards the midline of the body

Diag. 15: LATERAL FLEXION

Lateral Flexion

Movement refers to side or lateral bending of the trunk and head.

Diag. 16: ELEVATION

Elevation

Movement refers to raising of the shoulders.

Diag. 17: DEPRESSION

Depression

Movement refers to lowering of the shoulders.

Movement in the Transverse Plane about a Longitudinal Axis

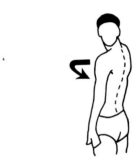

Diag. 18: ROTATION

Rotation

Movements include rotation of the head and also inward and outward rotation of the shoulder joint. Other rotations include:

Diag. 19: SUPINATION

Supination

Rotational movement along the long axis of the arm where the elbow joint is fixed and extended. The action is turning the hand outwards and upwards.

Diag. 20: PRONATION

Pronation

Opposite movement to supination. The hand is turned inwards and downwards.

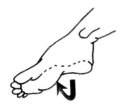

Diag. 21: INVERSION

Inversion

Rotational movement of the foot involves turning the sole of the foot inwards.

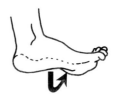

Diag. 22: EVERSION

Eversion

Opposite movement to inversion involves turning the sole of the foot outwards.

Diag. 23: OUTWARD ROTATION

Outward Rotation

Movement turning away from the body.

Diag. 24: INWARD ROTATION

Inward Rotation

Movement turning in towards the body.

Movement in More than One Plane

Circumduction

A circular movement resulting from a combination of several joint actions, i.e. flexion, extension, abduction, and adduction in the sagittal and frontal planes.

Diag. 25: CIRCUMDUCTION

Specific Joints and their Actions

The actions associated with those joints which are most commonly used in athletic activity are:

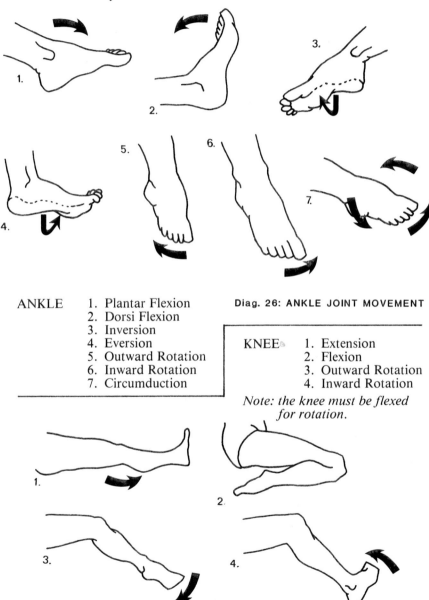

ANKLE
1. Plantar Flexion
2. Dorsi Flexion
3. Inversion
4. Eversion
5. Outward Rotation
6. Inward Rotation
7. Circumduction

Diag. 26: ANKLE JOINT MOVEMENT

KNEE
1. Extension
2. Flexion
3. Outward Rotation
4. Inward Rotation

Note: the knee must be flexed for rotation.

Diag. 27: KNEE JOINT MOVEMENT

11

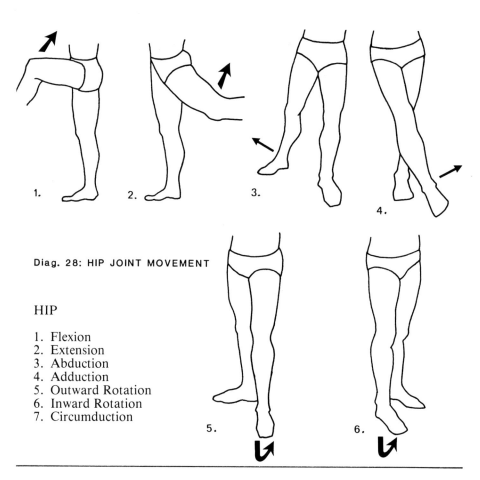

Diag. 28: HIP JOINT MOVEMENT

HIP

1. Flexion
2. Extension
3. Abduction
4. Adduction
5. Outward Rotation
6. Inward Rotation
7. Circumduction

SPINE   1. Extension
                2. Flexion
                3. Lateral Flexion
                4. Rotation

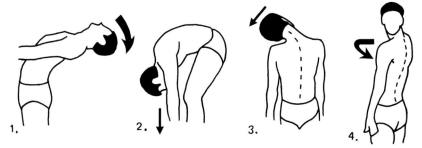

Diag. 29: SPINE JOINT MOVEMENT

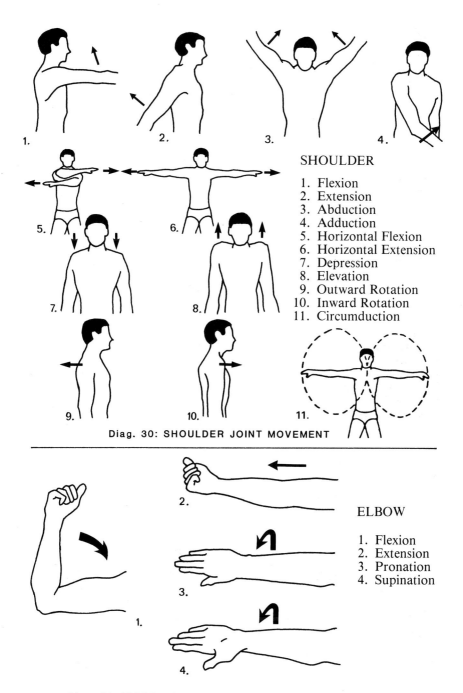

SHOULDER

1. Flexion
2. Extension
3. Abduction
4. Adduction
5. Horizontal Flexion
6. Horizontal Extension
7. Depression
8. Elevation
9. Outward Rotation
10. Inward Rotation
11. Circumduction

Diag. 30: SHOULDER JOINT MOVEMENT

ELBOW

1. Flexion
2. Extension
3. Pronation
4. Supination

Diag. 31: ELBOW JOINT MOVEMENT

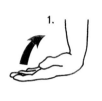 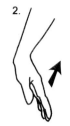 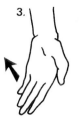 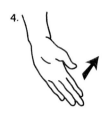

Diag. 32: WRIST JOINT MOVEMENT

WRIST

1. Palmar Flexion (Flexion)
2. Dorsi Flexion (Extension)   5.
3. Ulnar Deviation (Adduction)
4. Radial Deviation (Abduction)
5. Circumduction

FINGERS

1. Flexion
2. Extension
3. Adduction
4. Abduction
5. Opposition (Thumb
   moves across palm
   towards little finger)

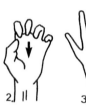  

Diag. 33: FINGER JOINT MOVEMENT

Factors influencing Mobility

An athlete's range of movement and his ability to improve that range are influenced by a number of factors including:

1   *The elasticity and extensibility of muscles, tendons and connective tissues of those muscles being stretched.* Improvements in mobility are gained by stretching muscle and its connective tissue which can be extended to 60 – 70% of its resting length. Beyond this, muscle fascia will probably tear. In practical terms, muscle and its connective tissue can be stretched up to 50% of its resting length.

2   *The extensibility of ligaments supporting the joint.* Ligaments provide the joint with stability. As they are plastic in nature, they can be stretched but do not return to their normal length. Stretching of ligaments will lengthen them and may reduce the stability of the joint. This is an undesirable condition. If ligaments are stretched, then those muscles which cross the joint must be strengthened to provide compensatory stability.

3   *Muscle hypertrophy, or any skin or tissue folds,* e.g. a "spare tyre", may reduce the possible range of movement by forming a physical barrier.

4   *Structural barriers of joint construction and bones* will make certain actions impossible (see "Types of Joints").

5   When performing active or kinetic joint movements where the protagonist muscles produce the movement, *the strength of these muscles* will influence the range of movement that can be achieved. Improvements in the strength of the protagonist muscle will lead to improved mobility.

6   *The ability of the neuromuscular system to inhibit or create contraction in the antagonist muscles,* i.e. those muscles being stretched. The neuromuscular system can affect the antagonist muscles in three ways:

a)   *Reciprocal Inhibition*
When protagonist muscles actively contract to cause a particular joint action, they send a signal to the antagonist muscles to relax. The contraction of the protagonist muscles actually inhibits contraction in the antagonist muscles.

b)   *Stretch Reflex*
Within muscle there is a special muscle fibre known as a muscle spindle or the annulo spiral receptor, which is sensitive to the muscle being stretched. When a muscle is lengthened, these receptors send a signal out from the muscle and back round again in a loop to signal the muscle to contract. This reflex action is a safety mechanism to stop muscle becoming overstretched. The muscle spindle is also sensitive to the rate and extent of the stretch and it causes a muscle contraction which is proportionate to both the rate and extent. So if a muscle is stretched slowly with a gentle build up of force, the reflex contraction will be mild. However, if the muscle is stretched violently, a powerful contraction will respond. This response is the reason why active slow stretching exercise should always be performed before any kinetic fast stretching movements are employed. The muscle has to be gently "persuaded" to stretch.

c)   *Inverse Stretch Reflex*
Contained in the muscles tendonous attachments to the bone is another receptor known as the golgi tendon organ. This receptor is sensitive to the build up of tension, which occurs in the tendon when muscle is either stretched or contracted. The golgi tendon organ has a tension threshold which causes the tension to be released when it becomes too great. This threshold is higher than that of the muscle spindle. When the muscle is contracting and the tension created in the tendon exceeds the threshold, a signal is sent to the muscle causing the muscle to relax. When the muscle is being stretched, there will be some muscular contraction caused by the stretch reflex. The combined

effect of the stretching action and the reflex contraction will cause a build up of tension in the tendon. The golgi tendon organ will then send a signal to the muscle causing it to relax. This will in turn allow the muscle to be stretched further. Often when a mobility exercise is performed and the action is held in the end position for a few seconds, you find you are able to increase the movement slightly. This is due to the inverse stretch reflex.

7 *The athlete's internal and external environment affects mobility.* Greater mobility can be achieved in warm conditions than in cold conditions. Alterations in mobility in different conditions can be observed in the following table produced by Ozolin (1952):

Conditions	Time	Result
After night's sleep	08.00	− 15mm
,, ,, ,,	12.00	+ 35mm
10 mins with body exposed at 10C	12.00	− 36mm
10 mins in warm bath at 40C	12.00	+ 78mm
After 20 mins loosening up	12.00	+ 89mm
After tiring training	12.00	− 35mm

8 *Recent injury to the muscle being stretched, or to the joint concerned, or a fibrous adhesion of an old injury* can cause an athlete to be restricted in a given movement.

9 *Inappropriate or tight clothing* will restrict movement.

10 *An athlete's age and stage of development* influence mobility. After about eight years of age, mobility starts to decline. Mobility training is therefore an essential part of all athletes' training programmes.

11 *Adaptation to habitual posture,* e.g. stooping over a machine all day, may reduce free movement in certain joints.

12 *It is generally accepted that women have better mobility than men.*

13 *If the movement involved requires a high level of skill,* the athlete may not be able to perform the movement due to a lack of skill, rather than a lack of mobility.

CHAPTER 3

MOBILITY TRAINING

A sound base of general and specific mobility is essential for success in athletics. In this chapter, principles of training and practical guidelines for mobility training are considered.

Principles of Training

Training to improve any physical conditioning, including mobility, must obey the three principles of training – specificity, overload and reversibility.

Specificity

To improve the mobility of a particular joint action, you have to perform exercises which involve that joint action. To improve hip abduction, for example, you have to perform hip abduction exercises. Performing exercises which involve other joint actions will not improve hip abduction as there is no transfer of training between the different joint movements.

Apart from a certain minimum level of all round mobility that is required by all athletes, an individual's mobility requirements are determined by:-

      i. the movement pattern of the athlete's event;

      ii. the athlete's present level of mobility.

A thrower, for example, requires good shoulder and spine mobility, whilst a hurdler requires good hip mobility. The types of exercise to be included in the athlete's programme are determined by the joint actions involved in the athlete's event. The amount of mobility required will depend on the athlete's present mobility status. Some athletes will need to improve their present level of mobility, whilst others merely need to maintain their present status.

The law of specificity is reflected in the athlete's choice of mobility exercises and in the amount of training he requires.

Overload

When an athlete performs a mobility exercise and stretches to the end of his range of movement by actively contracting his protagonist muscles, he is said to be in the *end position*. Improvements in mobility can only be achieved by working in or beyond the end position. Active exercises work in the end position. Passive exercises stretch beyond the end position as the external force is able to move limbs further than the active contraction of the protagonist muscles. Kinetic exercises use momentum to bounce beyond the end position.

The law of overload is applied to mobility training by working at or beyond the end position.

Reversibility

The law of reversibility applies equally to mobility training as it does to other forms of physical training. Training effects are lost over a period of time if mobility training ceases.

Mobility Exercises

In chapter 4, a number of exercises are listed according to the joint actions involved. These exercises might be active, passive or kinetic in nature and should be conducted according to these general guidelines:

Active Mobility Exercises

Slowly stretch to the end of the range (the end position) and hold this stretched position for 10 seconds. Release, relax and then repeat the action up to 10-15 times. When holding the stretched position, other parts of the body should be as relaxed as possible. Try to concentrate on relaxing the muscles which are being stretched. Concentration on deep breathing may help.

Passive Mobility Exercises

Mobility exercises which are performed without the active contracting of the protagonist muscles are passive exercises. A partner or some piece of equipment is used to provide the force which stretches the antagonist muscles. Using the simple passive stretch technique, the athlete's limb is slowly forced to the end of the joint action's range. The athlete concentrates on relaxing the antagonist muscles and, if a partner is involved, tells him to stop when the stretch becomes uncomfortable. The stretched position is maintained for 10 seconds. The exercise is repeated up to 10-15 times.

Passive exercises are particularly good at improving an athlete's range of movement as the externally applied force is able to stretch the antagonist muscles more than can be achieved by the active contraction of the protagonist muscles. Great care has to be taken when performing passive exercises, as the athlete does not always have full control of the force causing the stretching action. If a partner is to be recruited for partner-assisted mobility work, it is absolutely essential that he is a mature and responsible individual. The athlete must know that his partner will carefully apply the force which causes the stretch and that he will stop the movement when the athlete indicates discomfort or pain. **Passive mobility training needs to be closely monitored and controlled by the coach.**

Two other methods of conducting passive mobility are being used by a number of sports, although their use in athletics is not as common. These two methods increase the range of movement possible during a simple passive stretch by inhibiting reflex contraction in the antagonist muscles. As the reflex contraction is a form of safety mechanism stopping the antagonist muscles from over stretching, any attempt to inhibit this contraction not only increases the possible range but also increases the possibility of damaging the muscle or its connective tissue. Great care has to be taken when using these methods. **The partner needs to be more than just a mature, responsible person; he also requires to be a trained individual.**

1 *Proprioceptive Neuromuscular Facilitation*

This is also known as the PNF method. The athlete's partner slowly forces the appropriate limb through the range of movement. When the athlete feels pain or discomfort he tells his partner. The partner then holds the athlete in this stretched position whilst the athlete contracts the antagonist muscles as hard as he can. The partner holds the position which leads to the athlete performing an isometric contraction. This contraction is held for between 6 and 10 seconds; the athlete then relaxes and the partner slowly moves the limb a bit further until the athlete again indicates discomfort. This procedure is then repeated 3 to 4 times before the stretch is released.

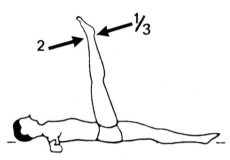

Diag. 34: THE "PNF" METHOD

2 *Stretch, Contract, Contract and Stretch Method*

Also known as the 3PIC method. The athlete's partner slowly forces the appropriate limb through the range of movement until the athlete indicates some discomfort. The partner then holds the athlete in the stretched position and resists his isometric contraction as in the PNF method for 6 to 10 seconds. Immediately following the isometric contraction of the antagonist muscles, the athlete performs an active contraction of his protagonist muscles holding this for 3 to 6 seconds. The partner then slowly moves the limb a bit further until the athlete indicates discomfort again. This procedure is repeated 3 to 4 times before the stretch is released.

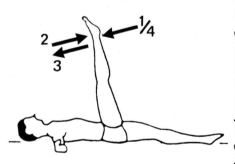

Diag. 35: THE "3 PIC" METHOD

There is a risk of injury if these methods are not used with care. Observe the advice given in the last paragraph on page 18.

Kinetic Mobility Exercises

Kinetic exercises are characterised by swinging the limbs which meet to constitute the joint backwards and forwards, or rotating them through their range of movement. Alternatively, the athlete can first of all perform an active or passive exercise and then slowly bounce past the end position. Usually between 10 to 15 swinging or bouncing actions are employed before resting or moving on to another exercise.

Guidelines for Training

Mobility training can be either general or specific in nature. General mobility aims to improve the range of movement of all joint actions and is intended to allow the athlete to accept and benefit from other forms of athletic training, i.e. speed, strength and endurance training. Specific mobility is more closely related to the actual joint actions employed in the technique of an athlete's event and in the movement pattern created by combining these actions. General mobility has an important place in the training programme of the young or developing athlete, allowing him to develop his overall range of movement and to take part in other training activities. There is little point in introducing the developing athlete to specific forms of mobility training until he is competent in the skills of his event(s). The mature athlete will include both general and specific mobility exercises in his training programme. He will maintain his previously acquired level of all-round mobility through the use of general exercises, and will use specific exercises including kinetic mobility and active mobility exercises combined with strength training. General mobility training will feature strongly in the general preparation period of the training year, whilst specific mobility training will have an important place in the special preparation period.

Training to develop maximum strength need not lead to a reduction in mobility. If mobility does decrease, then it is due to a lack of mobility training rather than being the result of strength training. All strength programmes should be run parallel to a mobility training programme. Some coaches would advocate the use of mobility exercises immediately following a unit of strength training in order to prevent residual tightness from the muscular activity. Others disagree, being of the opinion that mobility work should never follow exercise which causes local muscular fatigue. If mobility exercises are to be performed after other forms of training, care has to be taken as it is dangerous to stretch fatigued muscles. Only active, slow stretch exercises should be employed.

Strength training can be used to improve active mobility. Exercises which improve the strength of protagonist muscles enable them to stretch the antagonist muscles further and to gain a greater range of movement. Mature athletes can combine strength and mobility exercises, but these must be carefully monitored by the coach and must never be taken beyond the point of muscular fatigue. Resistance also needs to be worked against, at or near the end position, in order that strength can be applied throughout the range of movement.

Prior to performing mobility exercises the body temperature should be raised through jogging or striding or the use of other gentle warm-up activities. When warmed up, active exercises involving slow stretching movements should be undertaken first. The athlete can then progress to passive exercises and subsequently to kinetic and specific exercises which may be combined with strength training.

Mobility training should always precede those forms of training which produce fatigue, which explains why athletes include mobility work as part of their warm-up. Most athletes perform mobility work once or twice per day, either by including exercises in their warm-up or by undertaking specific units of mobility training. These exercises are usually performed in sets of 10 to 15 repetitions. Recovery periods between sets can either be active (i.e. jogging or loosening activities) or passive (i.e. relaxation without movement).

When mobility is first introduced only active exercises should be used, and the complete training session must be supervised until such a time as the athletes have conquered the skills involved and show competence in performing the exercises. Good self – and group-discipline is essential. Exercises must be performed exactly as instructed with the correct positions being maintained.

Cheating to relieve discomfort will not help develop mobility. Fooling about in sessions could lead to injury. It must be stressed that partner-assisted mobility exercises should take place only with mature and sensible partners and in the case of some of the more recent methods of performing passive mobility, i.e. PNF and 3PIC, the partner requires an element of training and supervision.

Mobility to Music

Mobility exercises performed to music have become increasingly popular. The music provides variety to the training programme, creates a rhythm to which the exercises may be performed and helps the athlete to relax whilst stretching. Most mobility exercises can be performed to music with 60/70 beats per minute. Edgecombe (1982) has suggested that the following instructions can be given at the start of exercises to establish the rhythm:

"Press and press and press and change"

"Press and reach and hold, 2, 3, and change"

"Reach and hold, relax and reach further, relax
again . . . see how far you can go . . . on your own
use the beat"

As with mobility training in other situations, the athlete has to be shown how to perform the exercise properly first and then can be left to repeat sequences of exercises in time to the music.

Mobility Tests

The range of movement in each joint action can be measured and expressed in radians, degrees or centimetres using flexiometers, goniometers, protractors or a simple measuring rod. There are, however, very few tests of practical value which are easily carried out by the coach.

Most coaches subjectively assess each athlete's range in specific exercises as being good, bad or indifferent. If however mobility is to be assessed objectively, possibly with assistance from the physical education department of an institute of higher education, then repeated tests made over a period of time are advisable. There is little to be gained in comparing the mobility scores of different athletes. Comparisons should be made with the athlete's previous score to see if the range of movement of particular joint actions has improved, declined or been maintained. Two easily implemented tests for spine extension and the hip flexion are as follows:-

1 *Spine Extension*

Lying face down with hands clasped behind neck. Partner holds down lower body including hips. Subject arches back by raising head as high as possible. Score is measured by the vertical distance the chin can be raised off ground.

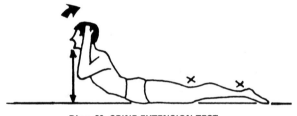

Diag. 36: SPINE EXTENSION TEST

2 *Hip Flexion*

Subject stands on bench with toes at edge of bench. With knees straight, the subject bends forward to reach as low as possible. The score is recorded as distance above (−) and below (+) the bench.

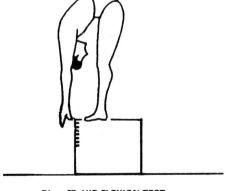

Diag. 37: HIP FLEXION TEST

CHAPTER 4

GENERAL MOBILITY EXERCISES

A comprehensive list of general mobility exercises classified according to the joint and the action involved follows. Each exercise is described and the movement is illustrated in the accompanying diagram. Some exercises involve more than one joint action. In such cases, the exercise is not repeated.

ANKLE

Plantar Flexion

1   Sitting on floor, arms supporting, press toes as far away from body as possible. Either single foot or both feet together.

2   Kneel on floor, toes extended behind; keep hips forward, thighs, hips and back kept in alignment. Slowly lean backwards, keep hips forward, do not lose control, head back towards ground. When you have gone as far as you can without collapsing, slowly rise back up again.

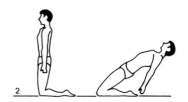

3   Kneel on floor, buttocks touching heels, toes extended behind. Arms support body weight and lift knees clear of the ground. Gently press back with buttocks.

4   Walking on tip-toes. Also try
walking on heels (plantar flexion),
outsides of feet (inversion), insides
of feet (eversion), toes in (inward
rotation) and toes out (outward
rotation).

Dorsi Flexion

5   Sitting on floor, arms supporting,
pull toes up towards body. Either
single foot or both together.

6   Keep soles of feet firmly on
ground. Slowly bend legs and
lower buttocks towards ground.

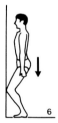

7   Face wall or box, stand arms'
length out, step back on one leg.
Keep heel of rear foot on ground.
Slowly bend knee in towards wall.
Repeat other leg.

8   Face wall, stand arms' length out,
    step back with one leg. Keep rear
    foot firmly on ground, heel down.
    Keep rear leg straight, let hips
    press forward to wall. Repeat
    other leg.

Inversion

9   Sitting on floor or chair, foot
    raised off ground, lower leg kept
    still, turn sole of foot inwards.

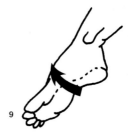

Eversion

10 Sitting on floor or chair, foot
    raised off ground, lower leg kept
    still, turn sole of foot outwards.

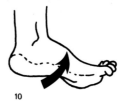

Outward Rotation

11 Sitting on floor or chair, foot
    raised off ground, lower leg kept
    still, toes moved outwards.

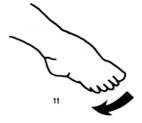

Inward Rotation

12   Sitting on floor or chair, foot raised off ground, lower leg kept still, toes moved inwards.

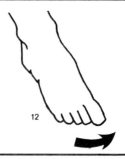

Circumduction

13   Sitting on floor, arms supporting, raise one leg, rotate toes in clockwise direction, then change to anti-clockwise direction. Repeat other leg.

KNEE

Extension

14   Place heel on bench, box or chair. Keep leg straight. Lean forward slightly, bend knee of support leg to lower hips. Repeat opposite leg.

Flexion

15   Standing on single leg. Pull free foot back towards buttocks. Repeat opposite leg.

Flexion

16   Lying on back. Raise knee towards chest. Keep opposite leg straight and buttocks on ground.

17   Standing upright. Raise knee towards chest. Avoid leaning back. Repeat opposite leg.

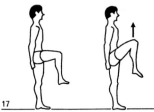

18   Kneeling with arms supporting shoulders. Raise right knee to right shoulder. Repeat for left leg.

19   Adopt front support position shown, keep palms flat on ground and legs straight. Slowly walk towards hands taking small steps. If pain sets in, gently press heels to ground.

20   Lying on back. Raise a straight
      leg. Grasp ankle and pull chest
      towards leg.

21   Sitting with both legs extended in
      front. Gently reach down towards
      toes. Keep back straight. Do not
      bend spine. Bend from hips.

22   Sitting on box or bench. Single leg
      with heel, calf, thigh and buttocks
      on bench. Gently, bending at the
      hip, lower trunk to leg.

23   Sitting with both legs extended in
      front. Reach down and grasp
      ankles. Bend arms and pull trunk
      towards legs. Keep legs straight.
      Bend from hips only.

24　Lying on back. Lift right leg up, grasp behind knee and pull knee to chest. Left leg remains extended and flat on ground. Keep right knee on chest and attempt to straighten right leg.

25　Sitting in a hurdling position. Reach forward to lay chest along lead leg. Bend at hips — not back. Repeat opposite position.

26　Sitting in a hurdling position. Reach forward, bending from hips, trace a semi-circle with hands moving from trail leg to lead leg. Repeat opposite position.

27　Two partners sit in hurdling positions opposite each other. Lead foot on partner's trail knee. Partners grasp each others hands. One partner leans back pulling other forward. Partner leaning forward should bend at hips. Repeat action with roles reversed.

28 Sitting upright with legs apart.
    Bend at hips and stretch forward
    to touch ground as far away from
    the body as possible or to lay chest
    along ground.

29 Sitting upright, legs apart. Bend at
    hips and stretch down each leg in
    turn.

30 Sitting upright, legs apart. Hands
    behind head with elbows back.
    Bend at hips and place right elbow
    inside left leg. Repeat with left
    elbow inside right leg. Keep
    buttocks on ground.

31 Sitting upright, legs apart. Bend
    forward at hips, chest towards
    floor. Partner applies gentle
    pressure to back to aid action.

32 Two partners sitting opposite each
    other, legs apart. One partner
    places his feet inside the other's
    feet. With hands grasped he then
    leans back pulling his partner
    forward, bending at hips. Repeat
    action with roles reversed.

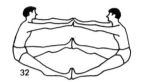

33 Stand in front of hurdle. Place
    heel on hurdle top. Keep lead leg
    and support leg straight. Bend at
    hips and attempt to lay trunk
    along lead leg. Repeat opposite
    leg.

34 Place heel of lead foot on
    partner's shoulder. Partner bends
    down to allow this. Partner
    gradually straightens up, whilst the
    other keeps his lead leg and
    support leg straight without
    leaning back. Repeat opposite leg.

35 Stand in front of hurdle. Place
    heel on hurdle top. Gently lower
    on to the knee of supporting leg.
    With knee now supporting, gently
    lean forward with upper body.
    Repeat other leg.

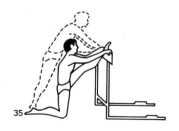

36 Walk in to place heel on hurdle top. Pick up bent knee and lean in towards hurdle during exercise. Repeat other leg.

37 Lying on back. Partner picks up straight leg and raises it back as far as possible. Keep shoulders back, buttocks, calf and heel of other leg on ground. Repeat opposite leg.

38 Sitting position. Place right foot beside left thigh as shown. Bending at hips, lower trunk towards left leg. Repeat opposite way.

39 Sitting with both legs extended in front. Reach down, grasp ankle and knee. Draw them up close to chest. Repeat other leg.

40   Place trail leg along hurdle top.
Keep supporting leg straight.
Stretch down supporting leg.
Repeat legs other way round.

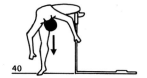

Extension

41   Standing upright, feet together,
arms by side. Raise right leg
backwards, keep leg straight. Raise
as high as possible without leaning
forward.

42   Lying face down, hands under
shoulders. Raise one leg straight,
as high as possible without
twisting. Repeat opposite leg.

43   Lying face down, hands under
shoulders. Raise both legs straight,
as high as possible.

44 Kneeling with arms supporting
    shoulders. Straighten one leg.
    Raise backwards as high as
    possible without twisting. Repeat
    opposite leg.

45 Adopt a stride position as shown.
    Both feet facing forward. Press hip
    towards rear heel.

46 Lying on back. Support weight on
    shoulders and feet. Walk feet in
    towards shoulders.

47 Lying on back. Support weight on
    shoulders and feet. Walk feet
    towards shoulders and hold
    position. Straighten one leg and
    raise it upwards and backwards,
    keeping hips high. Repeat with
    other leg.

48 Lying on back. Support weight on shoulders and heels. Raise hips as high as possible.

49 Using a box or horse. Lie on box face down with legs extending over the end. Raise both legs backwards as high as possible.

50 Reach over backwards to grasp a partner's hands. Partner provides support. Raise one leg bent and high, whilst keeping hips pressed forward.

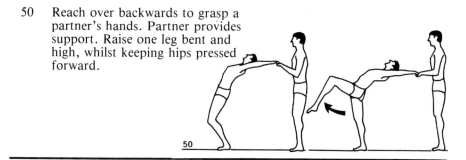

51 Balance on one foot whilst bending forward, with other leg raised straight behind and arms extended backwards. Lift rear leg and trunk upwards.

52   Lying face down. Reach back with both hands to grasp ankles. Pull on ankles to lift trunk and legs upwards.

53   Lying face down. Reach behind with both hands to grasp left ankle. Pull on ankle to raise trunk and left leg. Right leg remains flat on ground. Repeat opposite leg.

54   Lying on back. Lift hips upwards and support with arms as shown. Part legs to create a "splits" position in mid-air.

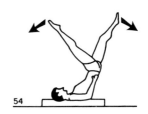

55   Lying on back. Lift hips upwards and support with arms as shown. Cycle both legs through a wide range of movement as shown.

56 Classical "splits" position.

57 Supported on right leg with right hand holding rail to keep balance. Bend trunk forward and raise straight left leg backwards as high as possible. Repeat opposite way round.

58 Stand on bottom rail of wallbars, holding on with both hands to a rail at chest level. Take one leg and extend it backwards and upwards as shown. Repeat opposite leg.

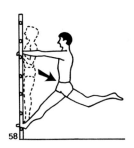

59 Supported on single leg and holding on to wall bars. Partner raises other leg backwards. Repeat with opposite leg.

60   Place heel on hurdle top or
similar. Gently slide supporting
foot backwards. Repeat other leg.

61   Walking with exaggerated action,
hips dropping towards the floor.

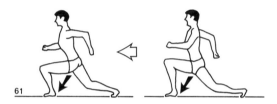

62   Sitting in hurdles position. Lean
back to touch floor with head and
shoulders. Sit up. Change legs and
repeat.

63   Standing on one leg. Grasp ankle
of other leg and pull up behind.
Move hand and foot away from
hip to stretch. Repeat other leg.

64   Place foot or knee on bench or box. Keeping trunk upright, let hip drop to stretch. Repeat other leg.

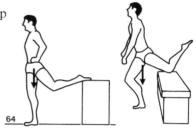

65   Lying on front. Partner sits on back and raises each leg in turn.

Flexion and Extension Combined

66   Standing on wall-bars or similar. Swing bent knee backwards and forwards as shown. Repeat opposite leg.

67   Standing on wall-bars or similar. Swing straight leg backwards and forwards as shown. Repeat opposite leg.

68   Front support on hurdle or similar. Swing bent knee backwards and forwards as shown. Repeat opposite leg.

69   Place foot on top of hurdle, placed at arms' length from person. Flex knee and press hips and trunk towards hurdle. Repeat with other foot on hurdle.

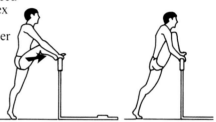

70   Sit in hurdling position. Stretch along lead leg, bending from hips. Then lean right back to touch floor with head and shoulders. Repeat in opposite hurdling position.

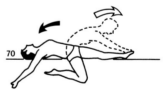

Abduction

71   Sitting with feet together, heels pulled in tight to buttocks. Press knees gently towards floor. Use hands on knees or grasp ankles, lay forearms along lower legs with elbows beside knees, to lever knees towards floor.

72   Sitting with feet crossed, heels
      pulled in tight to buttocks. Press
      knees gently towards floor.

73   Lying on back with legs raised,
      feet with soles together pulled
      towards buttocks. Press knees
      towards floor.

74   Lying on back with left leg
      extended and right foot drawn up
      towards buttocks. Right foot holds
      position and right knee is pressed
      to floor. Repeat opposite legs.

75   Standing looking forwards with
      foot on bench. Keep foot on top
      of bench facing forwards and turn
      hip away from foot.

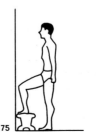
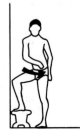

76 Lying on one side. Raise leg and arm as shown. Repeat lying on opposite side.

77 Start with legs shoulder width apart, hands on hips. Slowly slide feet apart to the side.

78 Sitting with legs wide apart, feet up against wall or bench on its side. Move hips towards wall as feet slide apart.

79 Hang from bar. Lift legs apart as shown.

80 Lying on back in a crucifix
   position. Keep legs straight. Raise
   right foot to right hand. Then left
   foot to left hand. Keep hands in
   position. Do not let them drop out
   of the crucifix position.

81 Supported on single leg with
   balance maintained by holding on
   to rail or similar. Place other arm
   to the side at shoulder height.
   Keep foot facing forward and raise
   leg towards arm.

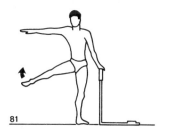

82 Place trail leg along hurdle top.
   Stretch down supporting leg. Keep
   support leg straight.

83 Legs wide apart. Squat down to
   one side, then to other side.

84   Kneeling on one knee. Other leg straight out to side. Stretch foot out and hip down.

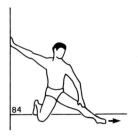

Adduction

85   Lying on back in a crucifix position. Keep legs straight. Raise right foot to left hand by crossing body. Then left foot to right hand.

86   Lying on back. Raise left knee and place foot to right side of rightknee. Keep back and hips on floor and press knee to right side. Repeat opposite legs.

87   Sitting with legs extended. Place left foot on right side of right knee. Place right elbow against outside of left knee. Press knee to right side. Repeat with legs changed over.

88   Squat down on single leg, with other leg stretched out behind and across to opposite side. Keep stretching to opposite side and let hip move down to stretch.

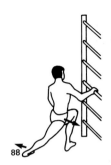

Abduction and Adduction Combined

89   Standing with weight supported on one leg. Balance kept by holding on to wall bars or similar. Swing foot of opposite leg from side to side. Repeat with legs reversed.

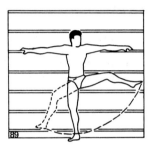

90   Standing with weight supported on one leg. Balance kept by holding on to hurdle or similar. Swing foot of opposite leg from side to side. Repeat with legs reversed.

Circumduction

91   Lying on back. Raise one knee. Partner takes hold of knee and foot and guides hip joint through a wide range of movement. Repeat opposite leg.

92 Sitting in hurdling position. Keep
feet in position and change to
opposite hurdling position without
moving feet.

93 Standing with feet shoulder width
apart. Rotate hips through a wide
range of movement.

94 Feet wide apart. Hold broom
handle or similar. From high
position on one side, swing down
and up to high position on other
side.

95 Feet shoulder width apart. Hold
broom handle or similar. From
low position on one side, swing
up, over and down to low position
on other side.

96   Standing, feet together. Bending at hips, describe as big a circle as possible with upper body.

97   Standing with back to wall-bars, weight on left leg. Move right foot through as big a circle as possible. Clockwise and anti-clockwise. Repeat with left foot.

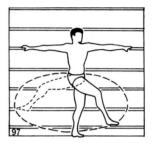

SPINE

Extension

98   Lying face down, hands supporting under shoulders. Fully extend arms, keep hips on floor and look up to sky.

99   Lying face down, arms straight out in front. Raise as much of body as possible off floor. Balance on hips.

100 Lying face down, hands clasped
     behind head. Raise knees and chest
     off ground.

101 Perform the classical "crab"
     position. If difficult, have person
     grasp partner's ankles. Partner
     then helps lift under shoulder
     blades.

102 Assume classical "crab" position.
     Walk hands and feet towards each
     other.

103 Lying face down with hands
     supporting under shoulders. Raise
     one leg and chest back to each
     other. Repeat with other leg.

104 Kneel with hips extended, hands raised above head. Keep hips forward and slowly try to bend over backwards.

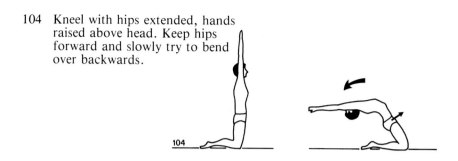

105 Sit in position shown holding on to wall or bar. Keep feet still, throw hips forward into extended position.

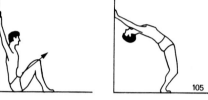

106 Lying face down with arms extended down sides. Lift shoulders, stretch arms back and lift thighs off ground.

107 Hold on to beam with both hands. Have partner lift feet as shown.

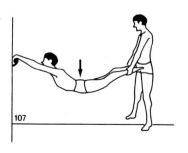

108　Lying face down, hands clasped behind head. Have legs firmly held to ground. Raise head, trunk and arms from ground.

109　Partners sit back to back with hands raised. Grasp each other's hands. One partner bends forward, pulling other over his back as shown.

110　Supported below at hips and above ankles, either on purpose built machine or on a box with partner. Rise up to look straight ahead.

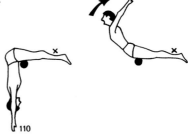

111　Lying face down with arms extended above head. Partner raises arms, head and trunk as illustrated.

112 Lying on back, legs and arms out stretched. Stretch hands as far away from feet as possible.

113 Kneeling with buttocks on heels. Gently lie back to place head on floor behind.

Flexion

114 Sitting with knees drawn up and apart. Grasp ankles and pull head and back forward and down. Curled action.

115 Crouch down, hands and feet in contact with ground. Keep hands on ground and slowly straighten legs.

116 Sit on chair, legs apart. Lean forward with folded arms. Reach down with head and arms. Alternatively have hands clasped behind head.

117 Sit with legs folded or crossed. Extend arms backwards. Curl forward as shown.

118 Sit with legs folded or crossed. Hold arms to abdomen. Curl forward as shown.

119 Lying on back, arms by side, palms face down. Lift feet above head to touch floor.

120   Standing with feet shoulder width
apart. Hands clasped behind head.
Curl forward to bring head to
knees.

121   Sit hugging knees as shown. Gently
move backwards. Hold position
lying on back.

122   Lying on back, arms by side,
palms face down, knees raised to
allow flat feet. Slowly curl up off
the floor. Head first, then
shoulders, then spine. Keep as
much of your back in contact with
the floor for as long as possible
whilst rising.

123   Lying on back, arms by side,
palms face down. Lift feet above
head and down to place knees
beside ears.

124 Kneeling with arms supporting shoulders. Keep shoulders and hips still. Curve back up and down as shown. Also side to side movement of trunk for lateral flexion of spine.

125 Lying on back, lift knees towards chest. Grasp arms around knees to hold position illustrated.

126 Use a chair lying on its back to curl over.

127 Kneeling with buttocks sitting on heels. Bring head down to knees and extend arms back.

128 Sitting with legs apart, knees
raised. Place arms through legs,
grasp feet and lever down.

129 Sitting with knees pulled into
chest. Roll backwards on to back.
With hands cross legs in the air
and then pull them close to body.

130 Lying on back, arms by side,
palms face down. Lift legs over
head. Now move hands back to
grasp ankles and hold position.

Lateral Flexion

131 Feet shoulder width apart. Avoid
bending forward or backwards,
bend sideways only. Stretch down
one side, then the other, whilst
looking forwards.

132   Feet shoulder width apart. Stretch
down one side, then the other.
Look to sky as you stretch down.

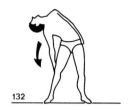

133   Feet shoulder width apart. Hands
on hips. Stretch to one side and
then the other.

134   Feet shoulder width apart. Move
head to one shoulder, then to the
other.

135   Feet shoulder width apart. Arms
above head. Stretch to one side
and then the other.

136 Feet shoulder width apart. Arms
     above head holding broom handle.
     Stretch to one side, then the other.

137 Feet wide apart. Hands on head.
     Stretch down one side to bring
     elbow to knee. Repeat other side.

138 Sitting legs wide apart, back
     upright. Place left arm above
     head. Stretch down to the right
     side. Repeat for the left side.

139 Kneeling on one leg with other leg
     straight and out to side. Stretch
     along straight leg to foot. Repeat
     with leg positions reversed.

140 Kneeling on one leg with other leg straight and out to side. Arm opposite to straight leg above head. Stretch over towards straight leg. Repeat with leg positions reversed.

141 Sitting on chair. Hands clasped above head. Stretch to one side then the other.

142 Sitting on chair. Hands clasped behind head. Stretch to one side then the other.

143 Lay a trail leg along top of hurdle or chair. Arm above head. Stretch over to trail leg. Repeat with other leg as trail.

144 Place hands on wall. One above
the other from a side position.
Push hip away from wall.

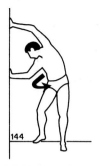

145 Standing feet shoulder width apart.
Hands clasped behind head.
Partner assists stretch down one
side then other side.

146 Leaning side on to wall-bars. Push
hip out to cause side stretch.

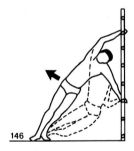

147 Suspended from wall-bars.
Swinging feet from side to side to
cause side stretch.

148 Standing on wall-bars. Push hip out to cause side stretch.

Rotation

149 Feet together, standing upright. Keeping feet on ground, turn to look round to the left, then round to the right. Move around as far as you can without feet coming off ground.

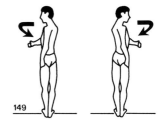

150 Feet shoulder width apart, trunk upright. Rotate head only to the left, then to the right. Move around as far as possible without letting shoulders move.

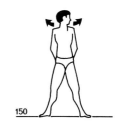

151 Stand with back to wall, an arm's length out. Keep feet on ground. Rotate to one side to touch wall, then to other side.

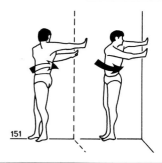

152 Holding broom handle or similar behind head. Feet firmly on ground; do not let them lift. Rotate to one side, then the other.

153 Bouncing up and down on feet with relatively straight legs. Turn shoulders to the right and feet to the left. Then shoulders to the left and feet to the right.

154 Feet apart, hands behind head. Bend over at hips. In bent over position, rotate to look to one side, then to the other side.

155 Sitting on chair or similar. Hands clasped behind head. Rotate to one side, then the other. Keep buttocks on seat at all times. Alternatively let arm on side of stretch reach back whilst stretching.

156 Holding on to a partner's hands or wall-bars or similar. Body fully extended, face down. Twist hips and legs to one side, then the other.

157 Lying on back in a crucifix position. Raise knees to chest, keeping shoulders on ground. Rotate knees to touch ground on one side, then to other side.

158 Walking with broom handle or similar over shoulders. As you step forward with right foot, trunk rotates to the right. As you step forward with the left foot, trunk rotates to the left.

159 Sitting in hurdling position. Rotate to the left, then to the right. Repeat opposite hurdling position.

160 Sitting with broom handle or similar over shoulders. Partner aids rotation to each side.

161 Partners sit back to back with extended arms touching. Both partners rotate to the left, then both to the right.

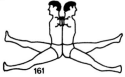 

162 From a "lunge" position, arms outstretched, rotate to the left, then the right. Repeat with other foot forward.

163 Lying on front in crucifix position. Right foot reaches back and up to left hand. Repeat left foot to right hand.

164 Lying on back. Raise straight legs
and hips in the air. Let one leg
extend backwards to allow foot to
touch ground behind head.
Without collapsing, let foot move
towards opposite side. Right foot
to left side. Left foot to right side.

SHOULDER

Flexion

165 Standing upright, arms by side.
Extend them straight back. Palms
face down and palms face up.

166 Reach back to grasp wall-bar.
Shoulders remain square. Press
shoulder down to stretch. Repeat
other arm.

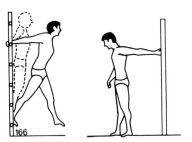

167 Kneel with hands clasped behind
back. Press arms up and forward.

168 Sitting beside step or bench, feet out in front, arms behind supporting. Keep feet still; lift buttocks and press towards heels.

 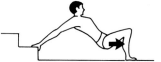

169 Grasp two ropes. Perform a backwards somersault to position shown. Front somersault to return.

170 Standing as shown on wall-bars. Let shoulders move out and down as illustrated.

Extension

171 Standing upright, hands above head. Extend them straight back, holding broom handle or without.

172 Lying face down with arms
extended above head. Press
shoulders to floor.

173 Kneeling, reach forward with an
extended arm and touch floor.
Keeping arm straight, push
shoulder down. Repeat other arm.
Alternatively use both arms.

174 Lying on back, arms stretching
upwards. Stretch them back over
head.

175 Lying face down on ground. Raise
arms only off the ground.

176 Feet together, legs straight; bend forward from the hips. Keep shoulders down and raise arms back.

177 Kneeling with one arm supporting shoulders. Keep shoulders down and raise straight free arm backwards.

178 Standing upright. Reach down back with the palms of both hands.

179 Sitting, reach down back with palm of one hand. Other hand assists. Repeat for other arm.

180   Leaning against wall as shown.
Drop shoulders down.

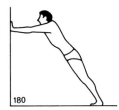

181   Step into "lunge" position. Stretch
both arms back.

182   Bend forward and grasp wall-bars
with hands. Press shoulders to the
floor. Alternatively, perform
exercise kneeling.

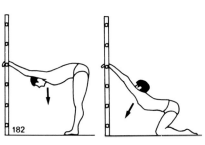

183   Hang in sitting position as shown.
Push hips forward and up, to
place shoulders on stretch.

184 Bend forward and grasp wall-bars. Partner, supporting himself on wall-bars, gently sits on shoulders to push them towards the floor.

185 Push hips out from wall-bars whilst grasping wall-bar with overarm hold for one arm only.

186 Standing on first rung of wall-bars, holding on at chest height. Stretch hips away from wall-bars and push shoulders down. Also partner can assist by pushing gently on shoulders.

187 Partners place hands on each others shoulders. Both bending at hips, press shoulders down.

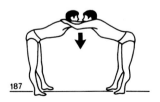

188   Kneeling, grasp hold of wall-bar or similar. Partner presses shoulders down.

189   Partners stand back to back. Reach behind, above heads, to grasp each other's hands. Both gently step forward to initiate stretch.

190   Partner takes hold of broom handle being held above head by extended arms. He also presses between shoulder blades. The combination is of pressing against the back and pulling back gently on the broom handle.

191   Hang from wall-bar. Partner climbs in underneath. Then raises you up by applying pressure to the shoulders.

192 Kneeling with back to wall-bar. Arms reaching over and back to grasp wall-bar. Partner pulls shoulders out from wall.

193 Sit against wall-bar grasping bar above head. Pull one knee to chest. Hands and foot provide support as partner grasps other leg and raises it upwards to pull hips and shoulders away from wall-bar.

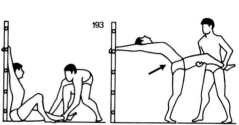

Extension and Flexion Combined

194 Standing upright or whilst walking, stretch one arm down and back, the other up and back. Alternate.

195 Standing upright or whilst walking, use the arms in sprinting type action. Use exaggerated action.

196 Standing upright. Reach one hand up back, the other over shoulder to grasp each other. Repeat with arm positions reversed.

197 Standing upright. Hold towel as if drying back. Move up and down. Try to move hands closer together.

Adduction

198 Standing upright, stretch arm across body. Repeat with other arm.

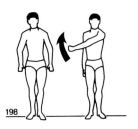

199 Standing upright, stretch both arms across body.

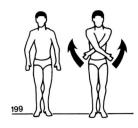

200 Standing upright, stretch arm across behind back. Other arm assists by gently pulling.

Abduction

201 Standing upright, arms extended, palms facing down, raise arms upwards.

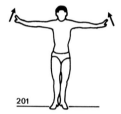

202 Standing upright, stretch forearm behind head. Repeat opposite arm.

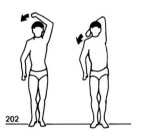

203 Standing upright, swing arms from side, up and above head.

204 Sitting, arms extended out to side.
Partner raises arms up.

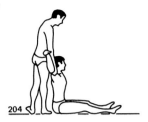

205 Place arm against wall as shown.
Press shoulder to wall. Repeat
other arm.

Adduction and Abduction Combined

206 Standing upright, left arm reaches
over to right side upwards whilst
right arm reaches to left side
downwards. Repeat opposite arms.

Horizontal Flexion

207 Standing upright, stretch arms
horizontally across chest.

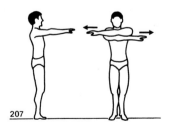

208 Standing or sitting, stretch a single arm across chest. Repeat for other arm.

Horizontal Extension

209 Standing legs apart, bending forward. Stretch arms back as shown.

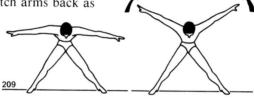

210 Standing, bending forward to support upper body with one hand. Other arm stretched back. Repeat other arm.

211 Lying on floor face down, arms outstretched in crucifix position. Raise arms up off ground.

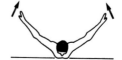

112   Standing with hands behind head.
Partner gently levers back elbows.

213   Sitting with arms outstretched
horizontally. Partner gently levers
back arms.

214   Standing with one arm
outstretched horizontally, hand
against post. Press shoulder
forward to stretch.

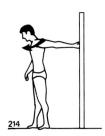

215   Stand just beyond doorway. Hands
reach back to sides to grasp
doorway. Pull shoulders away
from door to stretch.

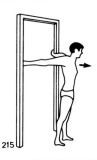

Depression

216 Place hands together behind back.

Elevation

217 Clasp hands above head and extend arms, from standing or sitting position.

218 Swing elbow up and out to side. Alternate arms.

219 Sitting or standing. Pronate arms and clasp hands. Stretch upwards.

Depression and Elevation Combined

220 Press shoulders towards the floor,
then upwards as high as possible.

221 Hold arms as shown, then move
arms up and down. Movement
from shoulders only.

Outward Rotation

222 Clasp hands behind head. Extend
elbows backwards. Sitting or
standing position.

223 Standing upright, arms bent out to
side. Stretch upper arms and
shoulders back.

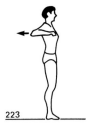

Inward Rotation

224 Sitting on chair. Clasp hands and
extend arms straight out in front
of chest.

Inward and Outward Rotation Combined

225 Standing upright, arms extended
by side. Push shoulders forwards,
then backwards.

Circumduction

226 Holding broom handle, or similar,
slightly more than shoulder width
apart. Rotate to one side, over
behind head to other side, back
down to front. Repeat opposite
direction.

227 Standing upright, arms fully
extended. Circle arms through the
widest possible range of
movement. Also holding Indian
clubs or similar.

228 Standing upright, place hands behind neck. Circle elbows through the widest possible range of movement.

229 Standing, arms extended out to side. Start with small circle of arms and gradually build up to largest possible range. Also holding Indian clubs or similar.

230 Standing upright, rotate arms across each other in the frontal plane.

231 Standing upright, with or without Indian clubs or similar. Circle arms in the frontal plane together. First clockwise, then anti-clockwise.

Palmar-Flexion (Flexion)

232   Palm towards forearm.

233   Standing, arms extended out in front. Use one hand to push other hand gently with palm towards forearm.

Dorsi-Flexion (Extension)

234   Press back of hand towards forearm.

235   Leaning against wall, supported by single hand with palm on wall, fingers pointed up. Bend in arm, then push away. Repeat opposite arm.

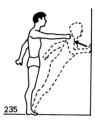

236 Sit in chair with hands on seat.
     Palms down, fingers pointed back.

237 Kneeling with arms supporting
     shoulders. Hands with palms flat
     on ground, fingers pointing back.

238 Place hands against wall in dorsi
     flexion position. Press forearm
     towards hand to stretch.

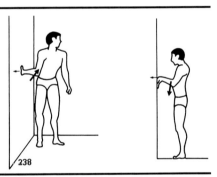

Circumduction

239 Rotate hand through a wide range
     of movement.

240 Hold object in hands and rotate through greatest possible range.

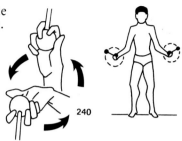

FINGERS

Flexion

241 Talon type grip action with fingers.

Extension

242 Extend fingers back.

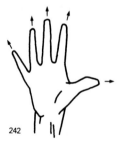

243 Fingers placed on table edge. Raise wrist and then push down.

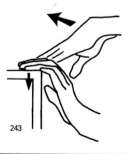

244   Press fingers together.

245   Elbows out, hands in, push ball
       away with fingers.

Abduction

246   Spread fingers apart.

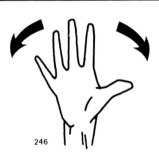

Opposition (Thumb)

247   Stretch towards small finger.

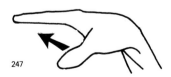

CHAPTER 5

SPECIFIC MOBILITY EXERCISES

A number of specific exercises for each of the track and field events are illustrated in the following pages.

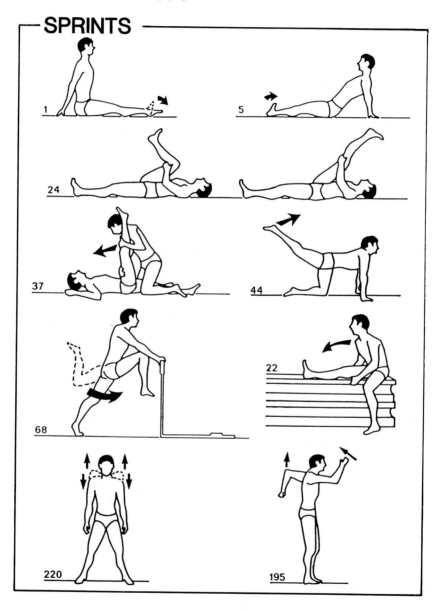

7

8

13

42

194

24

61

28

63

STEEPLECHASE

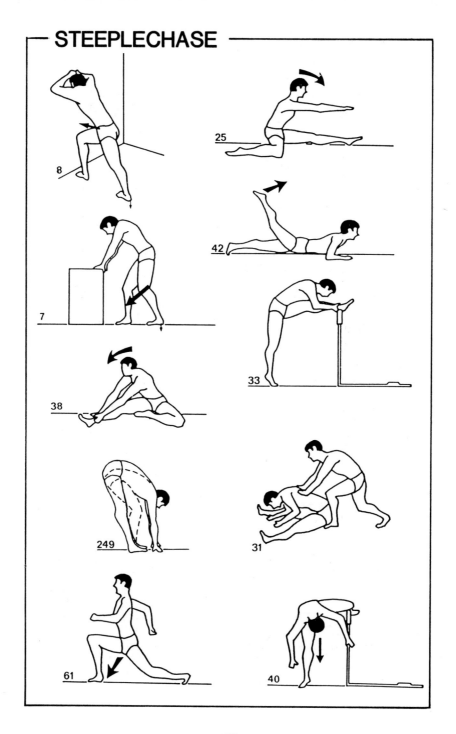

HURDLES

WALKS

LONG JUMP

1

13

4

23

72

24

42

69

162

45

227

167

63

TRIPLE JUMP

HIGH JUMP

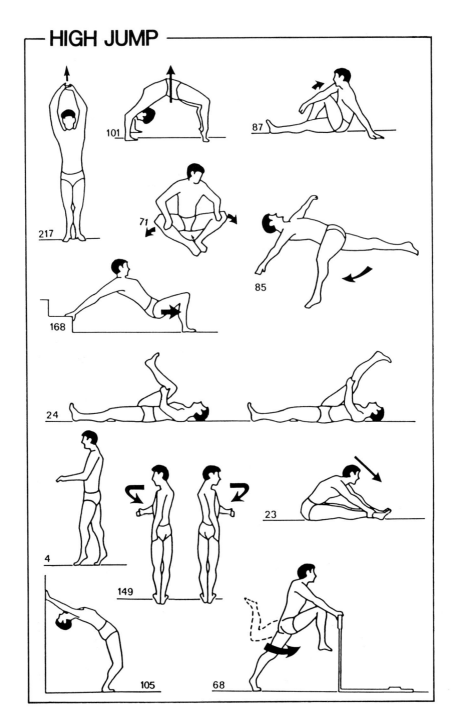

217

101

87

71

85

168

24

4

149

23

105

68

POLE VAULT

134

227

151

164

85

23

71

169

45

1

237

102

30

28

SHOT

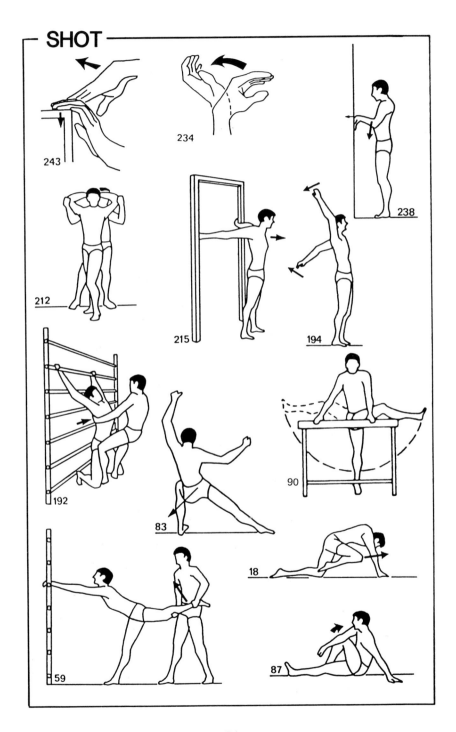

DISCUS

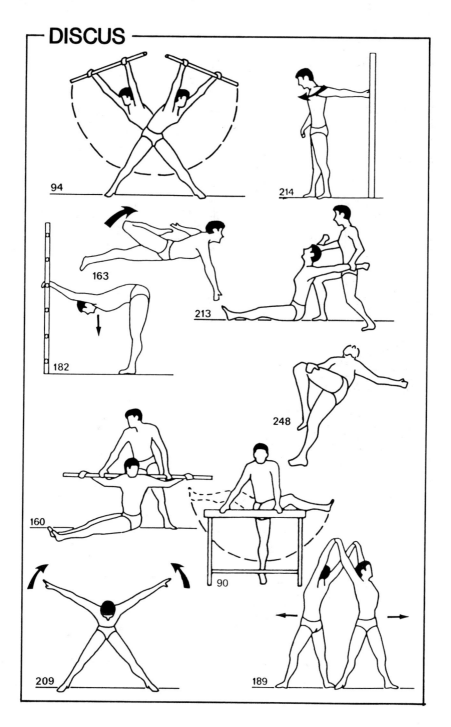

94

214

163

182

213

248

160

90

209

189

JAVELIN

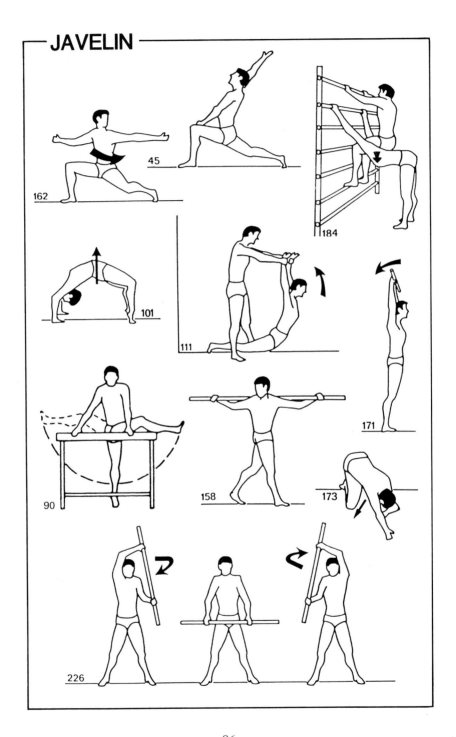

HAMMER

160

5

52

151

63

109

220

110